Maths Mysteries

My name is ....

....

I am .... years old.

I go to .... school.

I am .... at Maths!

Juliet and Charles Snape

Collins

A CALCULATING STORY
Digit Mystery

*A palindrome is a word or number that reads the same backwards or forwards.

The words RADAR and CIVIC are palindromes. The number 1065601 is a palindrome.

A spy listens in to Professor Panap. Can he discover the secret number?

You will need pen and paper to help solve this mystery!

PROFESSOR PANAP has a secret formu— locked away in his safe. The number needed to open the safe is changed ever— day and it is always a palindrome*.

I'm sorry, professor, I've forgotten how to turn the start number into a palindrome.

Write down yesterday's starting number.

That was 64.

Next, reverse the digits and add the two numbers together.

It's not a palindrome!

Can you use this method to make number palindromes with all 2-digit starting numbers? What about 3-digits?

THE Perfect Crime

The new gallery was having a special exhibition. The Gallery Director and her assistant were deciding how best to hang their pictures...

We'll put all the perfect numbers over there.

What about the others, shall we put them further along?

Yes, but let's have some down here as well.

BORIS the burglar was outside listening at the open window...

I wonder what a perfect number is... I BET IT'S WORTH A FORTUNE!

Boris climbed in after the gallery staff had left.

Which ones are perfect? They all look odd to me... I'd better take the lot!

As Boris was leaving with his swag...

GOT YOU!

Boris was locked in a storeroom whilst the guards phoned the Director. Boris listened in to the call...

The Director asked if the burglar had taken the perfect numbers.

... he was going off with a whole lot of numbers. I don't know which is which. What are perfect numbers?

PERFECT NUMBERS are very rare. They were discovered by the Ancient Greeks thousands of years ago. A number is perfect if all its FACTORS...

All its WHAT?

FACTORS! Factors are whole numbers that can be divided into another number without any remainder.

So 2 and 6 are factors of 12?

Yes. And so are 3 and 4. But to be a PERFECT NUMBER all the factors of the number except itself, when added together, sum to that number. 496 is a perfect number; its factors, not counting itself, sum to 496:

$$1 + 2 + 4 + 8 + 16 + 31 + 62 + 124 + 248 = 496$$

Hey, that's the same number code as the safe in the storeroom!

Interesting...

The burglar has got away with the fake jewellery.

It's lucky for us that they weren't PERFECT!

STOP! You're nicked!

The Ancient Greeks found only four PERFECT NUMBERS under 10 000. 496 is one of them and 8128 is another. The other two PERFECT NUMBERS are under 30. *Can you find them?*

5

The Missing Angle

PlayFast, the software and games company, is having a secret conference at a city hotel...

Bob, I'd like to bring you up to date on the new product before we meet the others...

The exciting thing about this new box of tricks is that it's a triangle!

Ms Duction, head of product development at PlayFast, was reporting to the sales chief, Bob Door...

Yes, Dee, I agree. A triangle looks ultra cool. What a GREAT idea. It'll be a big seller.

Lucas, an industrial spy employed by CopyZat Inc., a rival games firm, has been sent to find out the details. He is listening in from the adjoining balcony.

Um!... a triangle. That **is** new. I'd better get onto the boss straight away.

Back in his own room, Lucas telephoned his boss...

So the new PlayFast console will be a triangle. Find out what kind of triangle and the size of the angles.

Ok, boss. I'll get onto it right away.

Lucas made his way back out onto the balcony. The two were still talking.

What is the size of the third angle in the right-angled triangle?

It's 26 degrees.

Good. They're still talking.

Lucas had missed some of the details. He was worried...

Darn! I only know that it's a right-angled triangle and the size of one of the angles. I'll be in big trouble with the boss!

Much to the amazement of Lucas, his boss Mr Clid was not in the least bit cross.

> Knowing that it's a right-angled triangle and the size of one other angle, I have enough information to work out the sizes of all the angles.

> How can you do that, boss? Do you need a computer?

> No, just logical thinking and some deduction.

Mr Clid picked up the telephone.

> I want to put the CopyZat II into production straight away so that we can launch on the same day as PlayFast.

Launch day...

... at PlayFast Ms Duction introduces their new machine.

> We at PlayFast would like to show you the next generation of games consoles...

... on the back stairs of CopyZat Inc...

> We got the angles of the triangle right but nobody thought to find out the lengths of the sides!

> I'm sure it'll sell, boss. You can play a great game of ping-pong on top of it!

> I'll use that Jimmy Bond next time!

Mr Clid began to explain.

> First, I start with the fact that the angles in ANY triangle always add up to 180 degrees.

> I know that one of the angles in a right-angled triangle is always 90 degrees.

> So, I add 90 degrees and the angle I know (90° + 26°) and subtract the sum (116°) from 180 degrees (180° − 116° = ?).

> ... and you get the size of the third angle. That's fantastic!

Here are some right-angled triangles. *Can you find the sizes of all the angles?*

REMEMBER
- The angles in any triangle always sum to 180°.
- A right angle is shown by a small square in its corner.
- A right-angled triangle always has one angle which is 90°.

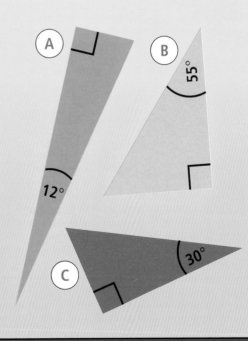

A

B
55°

12°

30°

C

Young Achilles was always short of money...

Are you coming to the market-place, Achilles?

Sorry, chaps. No dosh!

Fed up with being broke, Achilles went for a walk in the countryside.

Who needs money when there's all this nature for free?

Money spider

Feeling thirsty, Achilles stopped at a well by a shady tree. Perched in the tree was an old man.

Hello, up there. Is the well full of water?

Full to the brim, Achilles. Why aren't you at the market-place with your mates?

I'm strapped for cash. There are only a few coins in my money bag.

There's a way to make money that doesn't take any hard work or much time.

The old man continued.

This is a wishing well. All you do is run around it, say some secret words and the number of coins in your money bag will be doubled.

Something for nothing! I like the sound of that.

So what are the secret words?

To learn the secret words you must first promise to give me eight coins each time you go around the well.

That seems fair enough. I promise.

The old man whispered the secret words. Achilles ran around the well and called them out.

A loof dna sih

Achilles put eight coins into the old man's hand. He was then told another set of secret words.

Achilles felt his money bag rattle...

WOW! I've doubled my money.

Here you are.

Achilles went around the well again...

yenom era noos detrap

WHOOSH!!!

... and again his money was doubled.

Achilles gave the old man eight coins and then checked his money bag...

Here are your eight coins.

It's EMPTY!

Not a Greek sausage left. What's happened?

Achilles looked up into the tree but the old man had disappeared. The dosh-less Achilles made his way back home.

Hey, Achilles, what's a Greek urn?

This Greek didn't earn anything!

Achilles couldn't run around the well again because he had nothing left to double!

How many coins did Achilles have in his money bag when he met the old man?

Hint on how to solve this puzzle (upside-down)

Try working backwards: Achilles had 8 coins in his money bag after the second run but before he paid the old man. So if his money had been doubled how much did he have before he started the run? Now work backwards to find out how much he started the first run with.

Knights of the Triangle Table

Sir Cumference didn't get his own way about which shape was to be painted on the new shields.

If you won't agree with my suggestions then I'm off! And I'm taking my 'Round Table' with me!

Sir Cumference stormed out taking his table with him. The six remaining knights began to consider what to do...

We'll have to get a new table.

And it should be a different shape.

Where's Mavis?

Mavis, the mathemagician, appeared...

Whoosh!!!

How about a triangle?

What kind of triangle?

Are there different sorts?

Mavis opened her book.

Look here.

Triangle
3 points, not in a line, joined by 3 straight lines. The angles of a triangle always sum to 180°

Triangles are described according to the sizes of their angles...

equilateral
All angles are equal.

isosceles
Two angles are equal.

scalene
No angles are equal.

right-angled
One of the angles is 90°.

obtuse-angled
One of the angles is greater than 90°.

acute-angled
Angles are less than 90°.

Could a triangle be obtuse-angled and isosceles?
Could a triangle be scalene and acute-angled?

Mavis gave two tests...

Test 1

Which set of dots produces:
(d) a right-angled triangle?
(e) an obtuse-angled triangle?
(f) an acute-angled triangle?

Test 2

Which one doesn't make a triangle?

Join each set of points with three straight lines. Which set doesn't make a triangle?

Which triangle is:
(a) equilateral?
(b) scalene?
(c) isosceles?

(1) (2) (3) (4)

(5) (6) (7) (8)

Use tracing paper and join the dots. You can use a protractor to check if you are right.

With Mavis' help it was agreed that an equilateral triangle was the best shape for their new table. The knights would sit two a side. Now, back to the question of designs for the new shields...

I fancy a square.

Why don't I paint a different triangle pattern on each shield so that you each have a different design?

A dragon.

A rose would be nice.

How about stripes?

The knights thought Mavis' idea was splendid. So she set about painting designs with triangles on each of the six shields.

Then she wrote a description for each of her designs. The knights had a lottery to choose which shield each one would get.

POLYGON

The design on my shield is made using an equilateral triangle and a right-angled triangle.

Sir Amble
A

The design on my shield is made using two right-angled triangles.

Sir Bramble
B

The design on my shield is made using one acute-angled triangle and one obtuse-angled triangle.

E
Sir Eggum

The design on my shield is made using two obtuse-angled isosceles triangles.

C
Sir Crumble

The design on my shield is made using two isosceles triangles which are not obtuse-angled.

D
Sir Dumble

F
Sir Fumble

The design on my shield is made using two equilateral triangles.

Which shield?

A	B	C	D	E	F

Can you work out which shield each knight got?

WHICH AVERAGE?

Finding an average isn't always easy. You need to know whether you want the mean, the median or the mode.

Pro-consul Loonius has ordered the sculptor Billius to the palace.

I want you to make a giant statue of the goddess Isis as a birthday present for my mum.

How 'giant' would you like the statue to be, Pro-consul?

I want it to be EXACTLY ten times as tall as the height of the AVERAGE Pomposium woman!

Now get on with it!

Outside the palace Billius' wife Shortia waited for him.

The Pro-consul wants an average statue. He says I'm just the man to do it.

On the way home, Billi... chatted to Shortia...

There are three typ... of average. Looniu... probably wants you... use the MEAN.

What do you mean?

I'll show you whe... we get home.

Back at home Shortia set about measuring all the women in the household including herself.

Tallia → Shortia ↓ ↓ Vannia Odessia Pannia ↓

Tallia, you've grown another uncia*.

* The Romans measured in feet (pes) and inches (uncia). There were 12 uncia in a pes (uncia means a twelfth part). An uncia was 2.43 cm.

Shortia made a list which she showed to Billius.

NAME	Height (uncia)
Tallia (youngest daughter)	71
Me (Shortia)	53
Vannia (eldest daughter)	67
Pannia (cook)	53
Odessia (gran)	56
total	300

You get the MEAN average by adding all the heights together, then dividing the total by the numb... of people in the sample.

So, 300 ÷ 5 gives a mean average of 60 uncia.

I multiply 60 by 10 to get the size of the statue.

Billius sent off an order to the quarry for a piece of marble 50 pedes high. He then settled down to a relaxing bath.

Dad, Loonius might have wanted you to use the MEDIAN average.

What's the median average?

If you line up the sample in order of height, whichever comes in the middle is the average.

Billius hurriedly did some more calculations and sent off another order to the quarry.

median (middle)

Take this to the quarry.

(1) Can you work out which block of marble was based on the mean?

(2) Which was based on the median?

(3) Which was based on the mode?

CURIOUS NUMBER
– a mystery to investigate!

Aki and Isako were waiting for the Tokyo train.

You will need pen and paper to investigate this curious mystery...

IT ONLY TAKES 20 MINUTES.

HERE IT COMES!

As the train was leaving...

UH?

PLEASE CAN YOU TAKE THIS TO PROFESSOR SAWANO AT THE UNIVERSITY?

WHO SHALL I SAY IT IS FROM?

SHE WILL KNOW!

The stranger threw a package to Aki.

AKI! YOU HAVE DROPPED IT!

WHAT ARE THOSE NUMBERS?

CRACK

IT HAS BROKEN! QUICK, ISAKO, HELP ME PICK UP THE PIECES.

SMASA!

PUT THEM IN YOUR BAG, ISAKO. PROFESSOR SAWANO WILL KNOW WHAT THEY MEAN!

20 minutes later.

IT IS ONLY A SHORT WALK TO THE UNIVERSITY.

IT IS FROM MY NEPHEW, JIRO.

IF I FIT THE PIECES TOGETHER...

YOU GET 6174.

WHICH IS A VERY CURIOUS 4-DIGIT NUMBER!

Professor Sawano began explaining...

ISAKO, GIVE ME A 4-DIGIT NUMBER.

5364

STAGE 1: REARRANGE IT IN DESCENDING ORDER, LARGEST DIGIT FIRST...

SO IT READS 6543

STAGE 2: REVERSE IT...

... AND STAGE 3: SUBTRACT THE SMALLER NUMBER... THAT IS 6543 - 3456...

KEEP ON REPEATING STAGES 1 TO 3 UNTIL...

... IT BECOMES 6174

5364 original number

STAGE 1   6543   rearrange in descending order

STAGE 2   3456   reverse

STAGE 3   6543
        - 3456   subtract smaller number
        ─────
         3087

repeat stages 1, 2, 3
① 8730
② - 0378
③ ─────
   8352

   8532
 - 2358
 ─────
   6174
repeat again

APPLY THE STAGES TO 6174 AND YOU GET 6174 AGAIN! IT IS A LOOP!

stages:
① rearrange
② reverse
③ subtract

6174
7641
- 1467
─────
6174

I WANT TO TRY OUT SOME MORE 4-DIGIT NUMBERS...

...SOME WILL TAKE AS MANY AS 7 STAGES...

WHAT DO WE DO IF A NUMBER BECOMES 3-DIGITS?

ADD A ZERO.

WILL IT WORK WITH ANY 4-DIGIT NUMBER?

WE HAD BETTER START INVESTIGATING!

REMEMBER, EACH JOURNEY BEGINS WITH ONE SMALL STEP.

INVESTIGATE!

What happens with these three numbers? Which one only takes two stages? Which only takes three stages? Which number will never become 6174? Can you see why?

1234
7777
2004

Inspector Hutch, D.C. Rabbit and Columbo the sniffer dog are investigating...

In the Right Place

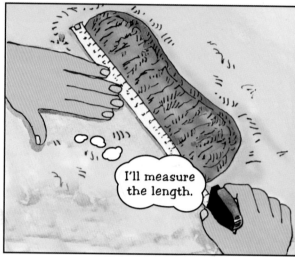

2	8	4	.				mm
2	8	.	4			cm
	0	.	2	8	4	m

Inspector Hutch has some suspicious items in the evidence store back at the station...

The decimal points are either in the wrong place or missing altogether.

Can you complete this list, putting the decimal points in the most sensible place for each item?

A Vintage car
£1299999

B Lamp height
1505 centimetres

C Cola
330 millilitres

D Table length
11 metres

E Population of London
75 million

F Watering can
35 litres

G Cat weight
25 kilograms

H Passport holder's age
185 years

I Designer jeans
£4099

So, 55 eggs altogether.

WOW! How did you work it out so fast?

Summing a series like 1 to 10 is easy. All you have to do is add the first and last numbers together. 1 and 10 make 11. Then multiply that total by the number that's halfway in the series... in this case it's 5.
11 x 5 = 55.

It works because the halfway number is the same as the total of pairs in the series that make 11...

1 + 10 = 11
2 + 9 = 11
3 + 8 = 11
4 + 7 = 11
5 + 6 = 11
$5 \times 11 = 55$

So, if you were doing 1 to 8 it's 1 + 8 = 9, half of 8 is 4. There are four pairs of numbers that make 9, so...
4 x 9 = 36
The sum of 1 to 8 is 36.

The next morning Sam found that 12 hens had laid in the same way as the day before ... the 1st hen had laid one egg...

Use Aunty Nell's method to work out how many eggs Sam collected from the 12 hens. Check your answer using pencil and paper or a calculator.

... and the 12th hen has laid 12 eggs. WOW!

So, where's our breakfast?

The Crumbles' Rumble Ratio

The Crumbles were working in the garden . . .

Wendy looked at a paint chart...

Freddie was sent to buy the paint.

Freddie took his time getting to the paint shop.

But Freddie had a problem when he reached the shop...

Freddie made his way home...

Freddie explained that Leaf Green had sold out but he could mix the same colour using yellow and blue.

Freddie found a large empty tin in which to mix the paint.

When they went inside the shed, they found the two tins that were left, one yellow and one blue.

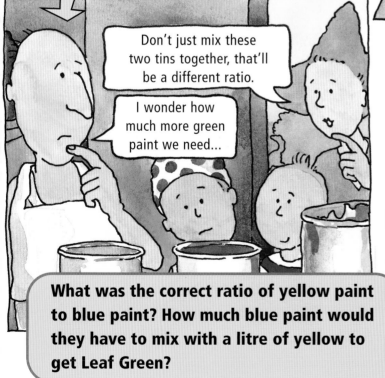

What was the correct ratio of yellow paint to blue paint? How much blue paint would they have to mix with a litre of yellow to get Leaf Green?

ICE SCREAMER

Paula's 'pushing-in' gives us a problem to puzzle over!

'Push-in' Paula would never wait or queue,
She always tried to get in front of you.

When twenty-nine people were all in line,
Between Paula and a divine '99...

Paula decided to use her best scam,
To cheat her way to the front of the van.

Each time somebody was served an ice cream,
'Push-in' Paula let out a terrible scream.

When all turned around to see why and who,
Paula sneaked past the next in the queue.

She did this every single time,
And soon was right at the front of the line.

"I want a '99!" Paula yelled out.
But the ice cream lady said, "No, you'll get nowt!"

'99!

GET TO THE BACK!!!

WAG! WAG!

"Nowt for the lass who can't wait her turn,
"Get to the back," she said, very stern.

So, if Paula was thirtieth in the line,
Can you work out from this little rhyme,
How many were served their frozen treat,
Before Paula met her shameful defeat?

SHE WAS PUSHING IN!

BLUSH! SQUIRM!

YEAH! SHE CAN NEVER WAIT HER TURN.

'Push-in' patterns

What a girl! Every time someone was served, Paula created a diversion and pushed in front of the next person in the queue. There were 29 children in front of Paula when she joined the queue.

How did the number in the queue in front of Paula change each time?

How many were served before Paula reached the front of the queue?

Use counters to help work it out. Write down what you find out and make a table.

You could start by looking at smaller queues. What happens if Paula is the 10th person in the queue?

Look carefully at your results. Are there any patterns?

Can you predict what would happen if Paula had been 50th in a queue? What about any length of queue?

Inspector Sherbert
AND the case of the decimal diamond

Lady Cumference's 5.5 carat diamond ring goes missing. Solve these six puzzles. Write down the number of each answer and find out 'WHO DUNNIT'...

Detective Sherbert was thinking about the case at Fraction Mansion, when the housekeeper stormed in...

Sherbert, you said you were giving me a 50% pay rise...

That's true, Mrs Fudge.

... but this note says I've only got 0.5 extra.

Clue A

What's the difference between 50% and 0.5?

(1) Lots.

(2) They are both the same.

(3) 45%

(4) They are almost the same.

Sherbert was racking up for a game of decimal snooker.

Umm? Some of the numbers on the balls have rubbed off.

Clue B

Each pair of balls sums to make a decimal number on the ball above:

$$0.2 + ? = 0.3$$

From the few numbers given, can you work out which number should be on the top ball?

(5) 3   (6) 3.5

(7) 2.2   (8) 1.8

0.7

0.3   0.3

0.2   0.1

Mrs Fudge said she was too upset to make tea, so Sherbert went to the local tavern to get some food.

It's a bit crowded in here. I'll go and get a fish supper.

B I've got 0.5 of a litre left.

C I've only drunk 0.25 of a litre.

D There's 0.6 of a litre left in my glass.

A I've drunk 0.75 of a litre.

E My glass would be full if you put in 0.35 of a litre.

1   2   3   4   5

Clue C

Match the person to the glass. Which is the list of correct matches? (Each glass holds a litre.)

(9) (A) 4, (B) 1, (C) 2, (D) 5, (E) 3

(10) (A) 4, (B) 5, (C) 1, (D) 2, (E) 3

(11) (A) 1, (B) 4, (C) 5, (D) 2, (E) 3

(12) (A) 3, (B) 4, (C) 5, (D) 2, (E) 1

A carat is a measure of the weight of precious stones like diamonds. One carat is equal to 0.2 gram.

Outside the Seashell Fish Bar, Sergeant Liquorice from Scotland Yard had rounded up some suspects...

TELEGRAM **GPO**

Sergeant Liquorice

Message: DIAMOND STILL MISSING STOP
SUSPECT BUTLER STOP HE IS MEETING
PALS OUTSIDE SEASHELL TONIGHT STOP

From: Sir Cumference Fraction Mansion

They're all claiming to be the butler.

How much wine is there in a normal bottle?

A 0.75 millilitres.

B 1.75 litres.

C 0.75 of a litre.

D 75 litres.

I say, Inspector Sherbert, any butler should know that!

Clue D

Which suspect gave the correct answer?

(13) A   (14) B   (15) C   (16) D

Back at home, Inspector Sherbert practised his safe-cracking skills...

Clue E

Which of these **can't** be made by adding together a pair of decimal numbers on the dial?

(17) one   (20) four

(18) two   (21) five

(19) three   (22) six

Dial numbers: 0.45, 0.25, 2.15, 1.9, 3.65, 2.7, 1.65, 0.75, 0.85, 3.1, 2.35, 1.3

$$\text{magnifier} + \text{magnifier} + \text{magnifier} + \text{magnifier} = 0.4$$
$$\text{pipe} + \text{magnifier} + \text{pipe} + \text{tick} = 0.7$$
$$\text{pipe} + \text{tick} + \text{hat} + \text{hat} = 1$$
$$\text{tick} + \text{hat} + \text{magnifier} + \text{hat} = ?$$

Clue F

What's the missing total?

(23) one point two

(24) one

(25) nought point five

(26) nought point nine

Sherbert solved the final clue...

Cracked it! Off to Fraction Mansion!

At Fraction Mansion, Sherbert confronts the three suspects...

I don't know if the culprit is Joseph, the butler, Julian, the gardener or Lady Cumference's niece, Juliet.

But using my clue decoder the answer is elementary...

Match the number of each answer you chose against the letter below it. If your six answers are correct, a 6-letter name will be revealed.

Sherbert's Clue Decoder

16	19	4	13	18	9	3	1	15	2	23	10	21	25	6	14	11	20	5	26	7	12	22	8	17	24
A	B	C	D	E	F	G	H	I	J	K	L	M	N	O	P	Q	R	S	T	U	V	W	X	Y	Z

25

Join Alice in two mathematical adventures...

Whose Bull's-eye?

Alice and her cousin Brad are visiting Crompton Castle.

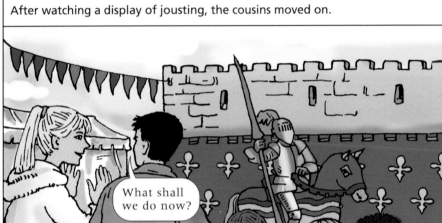

After watching a display of jousting, the cousins moved on.

What shall we do now?

Let's try that!

The pair headed for the archery compound.

You get 5 arrows each. The target is back there.

You've done this before.

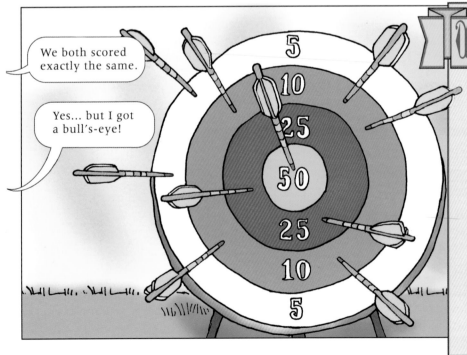

We both scored exactly the same.

Yes... but I got a bull's-eye!

Who scored the bull's-eye?

Take a look at the target.

Alice and Brad both managed to hit the target with all of their five arrows.

Both got exactly the same score.

Alice scored 45 with her first three arrows.

From this information can you work out which of the cousins got the bull's-eye?

Hint: add up the total number of points scored.

Counting Time

Alice and her friend Poona were out shopping.

The girls peered at the display case...

On the way home Alice and Poona stop to get something to eat. Alice studied her new digital watch while Poona got the food.

As the girls ate, Alice posed a puzzle...

Poona sketched out the digital numerals on a napkin.

Poona and Alice decided it was time to leave.

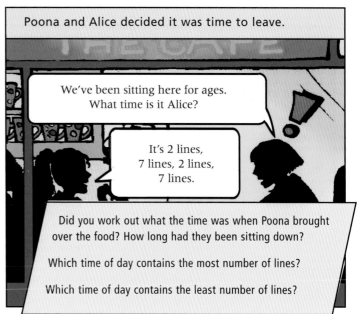

Did you work out what the time was when Poona brought over the food? How long had they been sitting down?

Which time of day contains the most number of lines?

Which time of day contains the least number of lines?

Splogies and Tabbies

Two types of frog live in the pond: Splogies and Tabbies.

All Splogies have spots and all Tabbies have stripes. The frogs have either 2 eyes or 3 eyes.

Some frogs always tell the truth and some always tell lies.

To sum up:
- Splogies with 2 eyes always lie
- Tabbies with 2 eyes always tell the truth
- Splogies with 3 eyes always tell the truth
- Tabbies with 3 eyes always lie.

Can you use this information to answer the questions? You will need to think carefully.

1. How many eyes?

2. Spots or stripes?

3. How many eyes?

4. Spots or stripes?

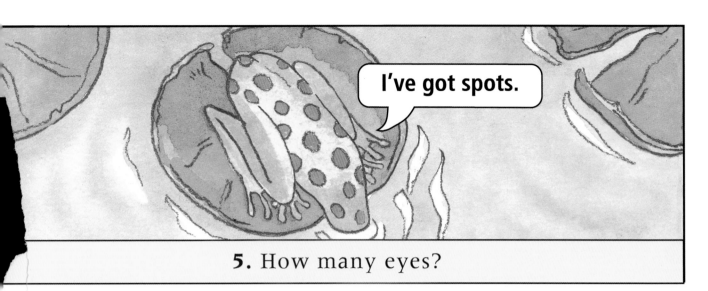

5. How many eyes?

6. How many eyes?

7. Are both these two questions enough to find out what type of frog this is?

(A) "Do you have stripes?"

(B) "Do you have 2 eyes?"

Solutions

This is where you can check your answers, or see how to solve a puzzle if you've got stuck. At the end of each we tell you which part of the Maths curriculum you're practising.

Digit Mystery (pages 2 and 3)

$$\begin{array}{r} 1801200002107 \\ + \ 7012000021081 \\ \hline 8813200023188 \end{array}$$

It becomes a palindrome after only one stage.

All 2-digit numbers become palindromes. Most only take one or two stages but 89 (and its reverse 98) takes 24 stages.

All 3-digit numbers become palindromes eventually apart from 196. Even with powerful computers a palindrome from 196 has not been found, but mathematicians can't be sure that one will never be found.

> Maths topic: Numbers and the number system, symmetry

The Perfect Crime (pages 4 and 5)

The two perfect numbers under 30 are:
6 (1 + 2 + 3) and **28** (1 + 2 + 4 + 7 + 14)

> Maths topic: Numbers and the number system, factors

The Missing Angle (pages 6 and 7)

A = **78°** (12° + 90° = 102°; 180° − 102° = **78°**)
B = **35°** (55° + 90° = 145°; 180° − 145° = **35°**)
C = **60°** (30° + 90° = 120°; 180° − 120° = **60°**)

> Maths topic: Measures, shape and space

Something for Nothing (pages 8 and 9)

Achilles started with 6 coins in his pocket. Here is how he lost them:

At finish of first run	6 × 2 = 12
After paying old man	12 − 8 = 4
At finish of second run	4 × 2 = 8
After paying old man	8 − 8 = 0

The secret words the old man whispered to Achilles are an old saying spelt backwards: 'A fool and his money are soon parted.'

> Maths topic: Solving problems, reasoning

Knights of the Triangle Table (pages 10 and 11)

A triangle can be both obtuse-angled and isoscele
A triangle can be both scalene and acute-angled.

Test 1
(1) Scalene
(2) Isosceles
(3) Not a triangle
(4) Equilateral

Test 2
(5) Acute-angled
(6) Not a triangle
(7) Obtuse-angled
(8) Right-angled

Which shield?

A	B	C	D	E	F
5	6	3	1	4	2

> Maths topic: Measures, shape and space

Which Average? (pages 12 and 13)

(A) Median (56 uncia × 10 = 560)
(B) Mean (60 uncia × 10 = 600)
(C) Mode (53 uncia × 10 = 530)

> Maths topic: Handling data

Curious Number (pages 14 and 15)

1234 takes three stages to become 6174:

$$\begin{array}{l} -\ 4321 \quad \text{rearrange} \\ \ \ \underline{1234} \quad \text{reverse} \\ \ \ \mathbf{3087} \end{array}$$

$$\begin{array}{l} -\ 8730 \quad \text{rearrange} \\ \ \ \underline{0378} \quad \text{reverse} \\ \ \ \mathbf{8352} \end{array}$$

$$\begin{array}{l} -\ 8532 \quad \text{rearrange} \\ \ \ \underline{2358} \quad \text{reverse} \\ \ \ \mathbf{6174} \end{array}$$

7777 can never become 6174 because all the digits are the same:

$$\begin{array}{l} \ \ 7777 \\ -\ 7777 \quad \text{rearrange} \\ \ \ \underline{7777} \quad \text{reverse} \\ \ \ \mathbf{0000} \end{array}$$

004 takes two stages to become 6174:

2004
4200 rearrange
0024 reverse

176

641 rearrange
467 reverse

74

Maths topic: Numbers and the number system

the Right Place (pages 16 and 17)

A) £12999.99
B) 150.5 centimetres
C) 330 millilitres
D) 1.1 metres
E) 7.5 million
F) 3.5 litres
G) 2.5 kilograms
H) 18.5 years
I) £40.99

Maths topic: Numbers and the number system, measures

Sam Sums Some Eggs (pages 18 and 19)

12 hens producing in the way described would lay **78 eggs**.

1 to 12
1 + 12 = 13
Half of 12 is 6 and there are 6 pairs of numbers that make 13:

$6 \times 13 = 78$

You can also check this by writing out the pairs:

1 + 12 = 13
2 + 11 = 13
3 + 10 = 13
4 + 9 = 13
5 + 8 = 13
6 + 7 = 13

Maths topic: Numbers and the number system, sequences

The Crumbles' Rumble Ratio
(pages 20 and 21)

The correct ratio of yellow paint to blue is 2:1.

Mixing half a litre of blue paint with a litre of yellow paint would give the correct mix.
Half a litre of blue paint will be left over.

Maths topic: Numbers and the number system, ratio

Ice Screamer (pages 22 and 23)

Paula's position in the queue reduces by two each time someone is served: the person served plus the person pushed by. So the number of people served before Paula gets to the front is 15 (half the size of the queue).

If Paula is the 10th person in the queue, 5 people will be served before she makes it to the front.

This table shows how a pattern emerges for queues with an even number.

Number in queue	Number in front of Paula	Number Paula pushes by	Number served before Paula
10	9	4	5
20	19	9	10
30	29	14	15
40	39	19	20
50	49	24	25

If there is an odd number in the queue, Paula has to push past the same number of people as are served; e.g. for a queue of 11 she pushes by 5 and 5 are served before she gets to the front.

Maths topic: Solving problems

Inspector Sherbert (pages 24 and 25)

Clue A (2)   Clue B (7)   2.2
1 1.2
0.5 0.5 0.7
0.3 0.2 0.3 0.4
0.2 0.1 0.1 0.2 0.2

Clue C (10)   Clue D (15)   Clue E (18)   Clue F (26)

Using 'Sherbert's Clue Decoder' the culprit is JULIET.

Maths topic: Numbers and the number system, decimals

Whose Bull's-eye? (page 26)

Brad got the bull's-eye.
The total score for both cousins was **160 points**
(2×5, 5×10, 2×25 and 1×50), so each cousin
scored **80 points**. Alice scored 45 with her first three
arrows ($10 + 10 + 25$) so she couldn't have got the
bull's-eye. This means she got 35 points with her last
two arrows ($10 + 25$). You can then work out how
Brad scored the rest of his 80 points.

Alice	Brad
10	50
10	10
25	10
10	5
25	5
80	**80**

Maths topic: Handling data, calculations

Counting Time (page 27)

Number of lines	2	5	5	4	5	6	3	7	6	6

Poona brought the food over to Alice at 17:48.
They had been sitting down for 30 minutes so the
time was 18:18.

The time of day with the most number of lines is
08:08. It uses 26 lines.

The time of day with the least number of lines is
11:11. It uses only 8 lines.

Maths topic: Measures, shape and space

Splogies and Tabbies (pages 28 and 29)

(1) 2 eyes
(2) Stripes
(3) 3 eyes
(4) Stripes
(5) 3 eyes
(6) 2 eyes

(7) Yes, you can find out
which type of frog it is
using both the 2 questions.

First question: "Have you got stripes?"
If the answer is 'yes' then it must be:
a 2-eyed Tabbie (true) or a 2-eyed Splogie (lie).
If 'no' then it must be:
a 3-eyed Tabbie (lie) or a 3-eyed Splogie (true).

Second question: "Do you have 2 eyes?"
If the frog says 'yes' to both questions you know that
it's a 2-eyed Tabbie.
If the frog says 'yes' to the first question and 'no' to
the second then it's a 2-eyed Splogie.
If the frog says 'no' to both questions you know that
it's a 3-eyed Splogie.
If the frog says 'no' to the first question and 'yes' to
the second then it's a 3-eyed Tabbie.

Maths topic: Solving problems, reasoning

Published by Collins
An imprint of HarperCollins*Publishers*
77 – 85 Fulham Palace Road
Hammersmith
London
W6 8JB

Browse the complete Collins catalogue at
www.collins.co.uk

© 2005 Juliet and Charles Snape

10 9 8 7 6 5 4 3 2 1

ISBN 0 00 721147 3

Juliet and Charles Snape assert their moral rights to be identified as
the authors of this work

British Library Cataloguing in Publication Data
A Catalogue record for this publication is available from the British
Library

Written by Juliet and Charles Snape
Consultant: Nigel Langdon MPhil, a maths consultant for the
           Royal Borough of Kingston upon Thames
Design, cover and illustrations by Juliet and Charles Snape
Printed and bound by Imago Thailand

Titles in this series:
Maths Explorer, Maths Mazes, Maths Mysteries, Maths Puzzles
To order any of these titles, please telephone **0870 787 1732**
and quote code **256V**.